D1484832

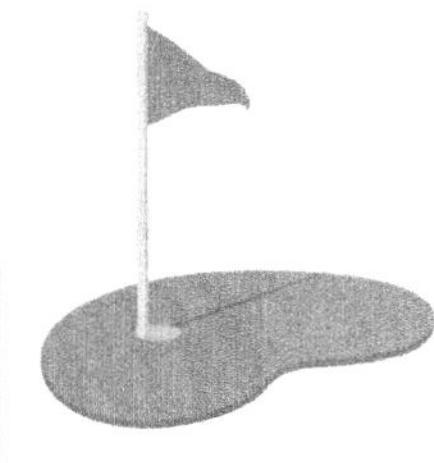

Hello and welcome

GOLF IS FUN AND ADDICTIVE, IN THIS GOLF ACTIVITY BOOK YOU WILL BE ABLE TO DRAW, FIND, SEARCH AND COLOR MANY GOLF THEMED ACTIVITIES INCLUDING STORY BASED MAZES- CHECK OUT OUR BACK PAGE FOR EXAMPLES (BONUS CERTIFICATE PAGE INCLUDED)

GRAB SOME COLOUR PENCILS, A PEN, PENCIL AND BE EXCITED TO COMPLETE THIS ACTIVITY BOOK.

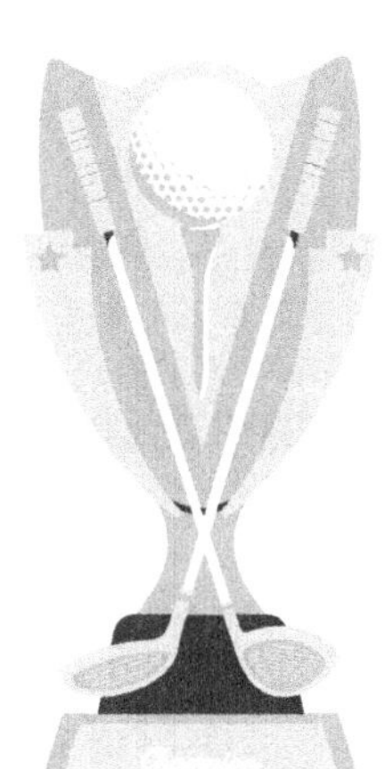

ACTIVITIES INCLUDE

- STORY MAZES
- COLORING PAGES
- WORD SEARCH
- DESIGN YOUR OWN
- DESIGN CHALLENGES
- BRAIN CHALLENGES
- MATCHING
- PICTURE SUDOKU
- GOLF FACTS
- AND MORE

THIS BOOK BELONGS TO

____

CAN YOU HIT THE BALL IN THE HOLE?

TRY AND GET A HOLE IN ONE

CAN YOU FIND THE ODD GOLFER OUT?

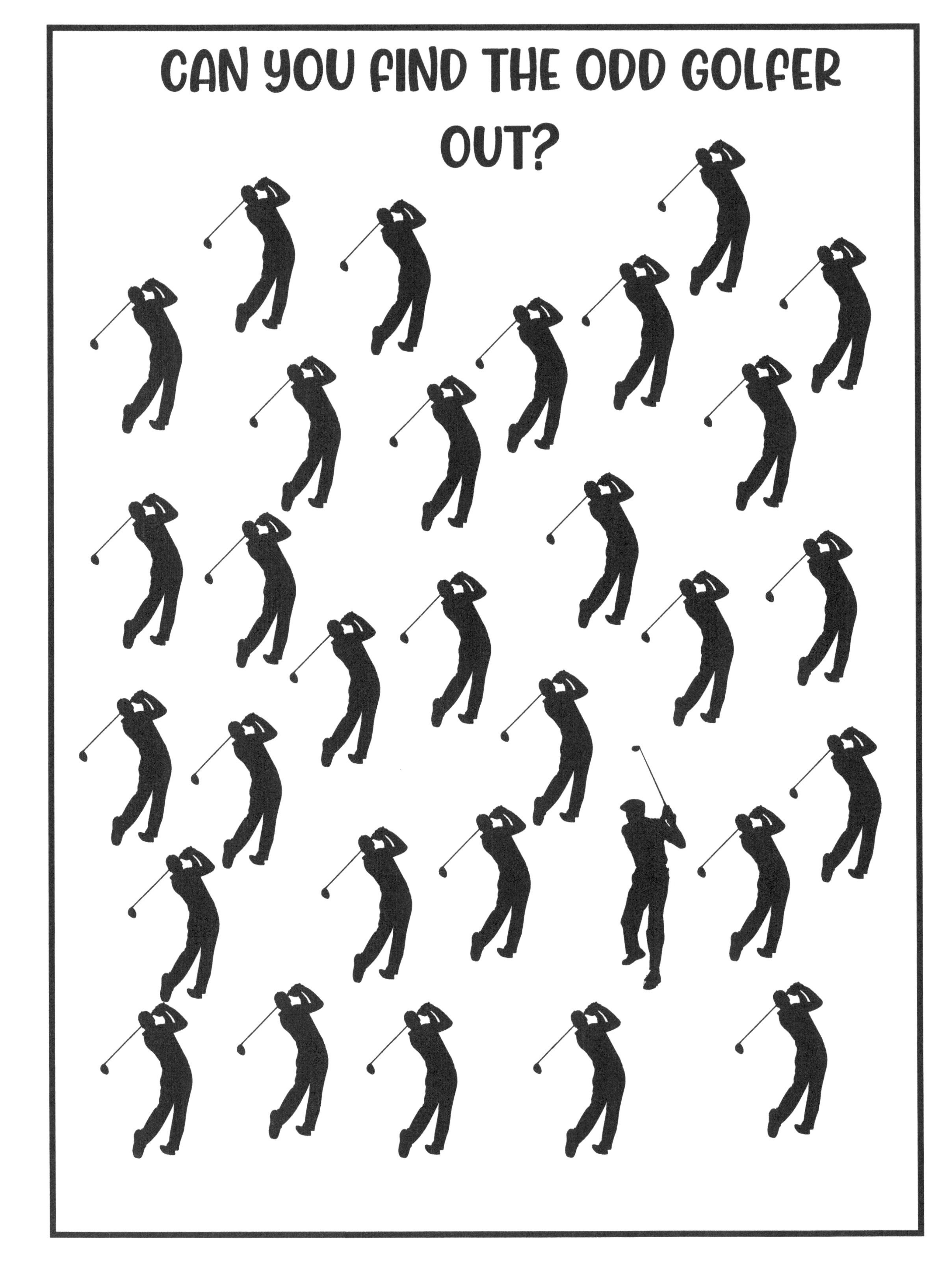

WHICH GOLF CART IS THE CORRECT ROUTE TO THE COURSE

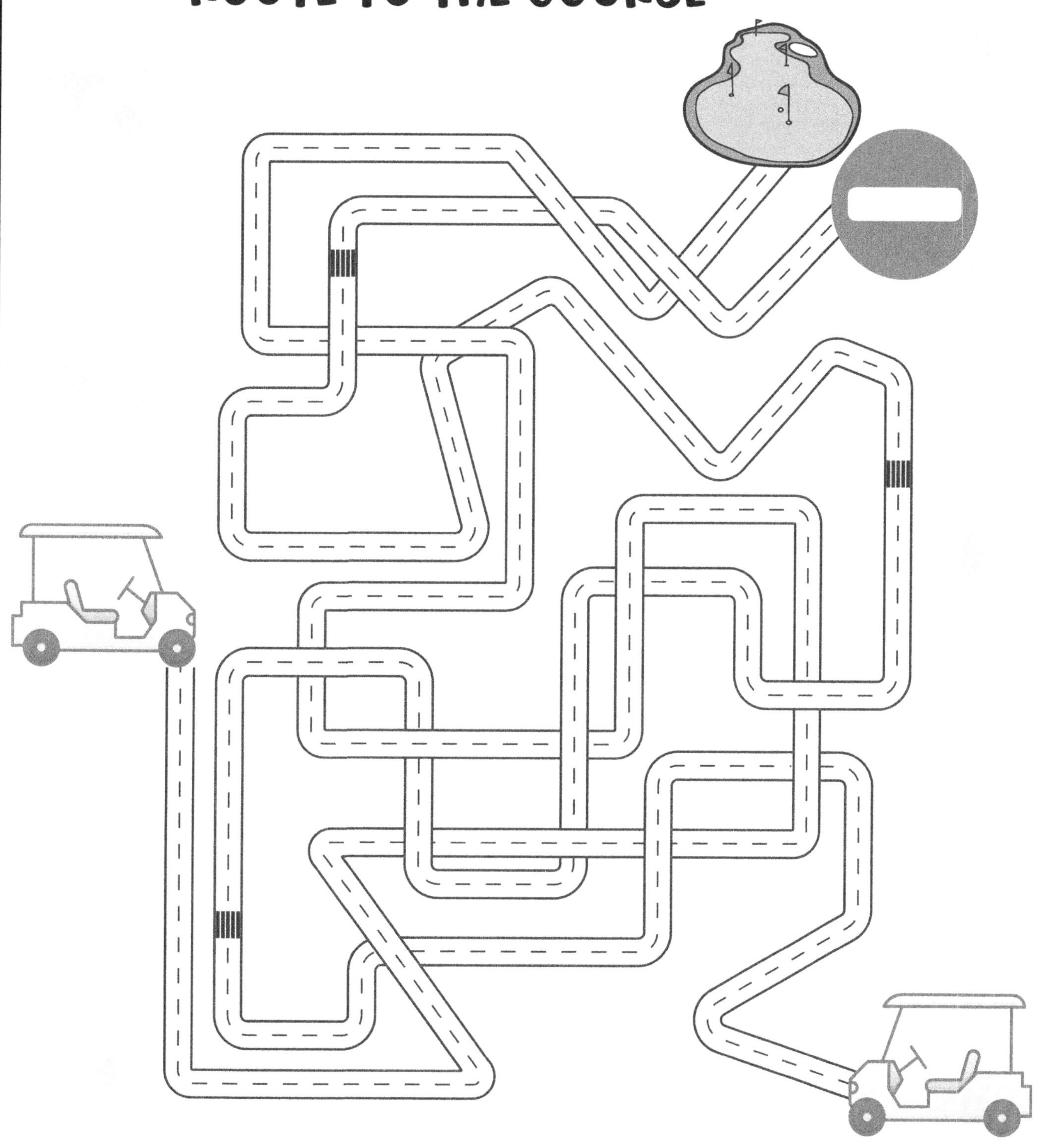

DON'T HIT THE NO ENTRY

CAN YOU FIND
CIRCLE IT

GUIDE EACH PLAYER TO THEIR ITEMS

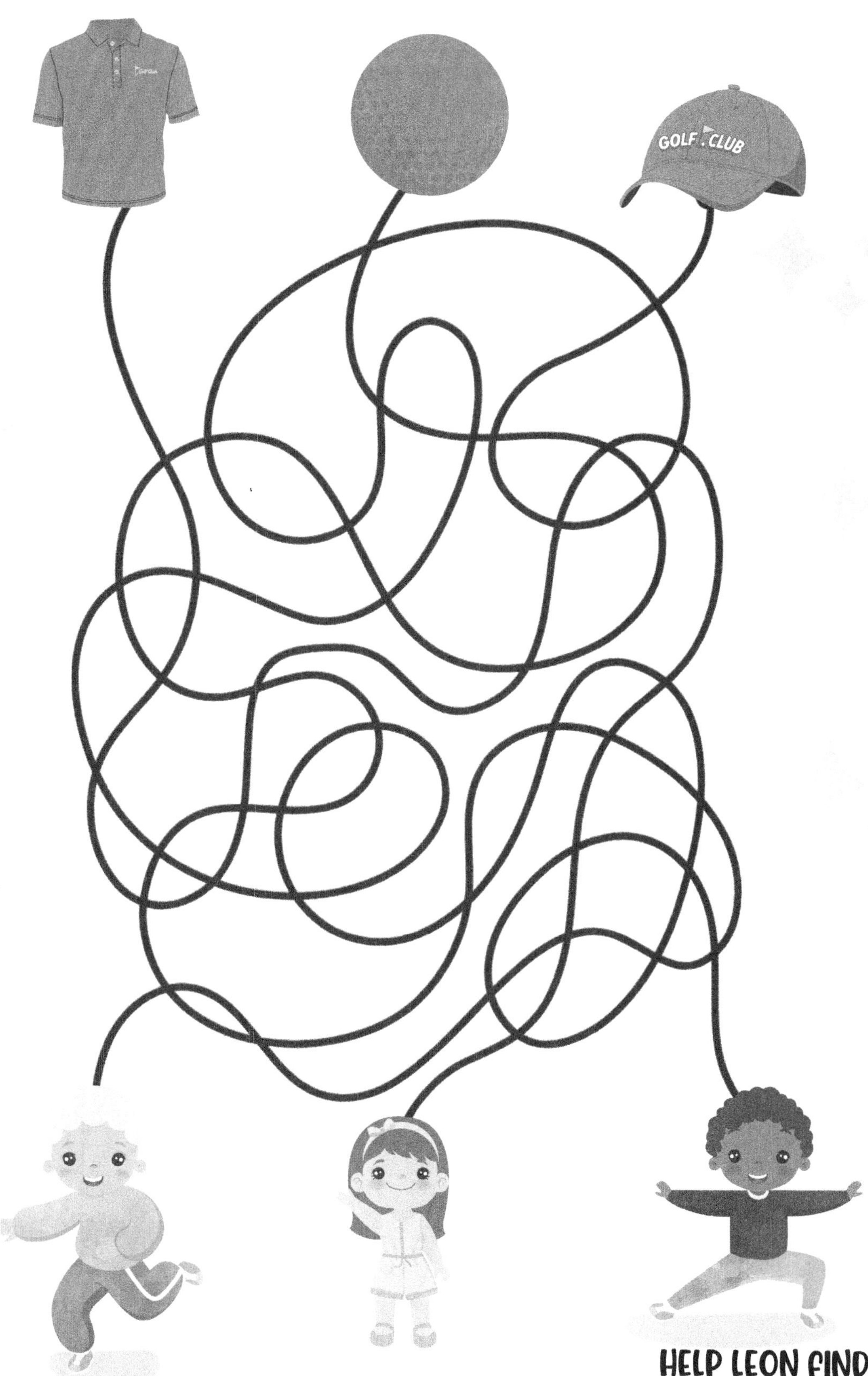

HELP BOBBY FIND HIS GOLF BALL

HELP ANNE FIND HER GOLF SHIRT

HELP LEON FIND HIS GOLF CAP

Solution 3

FIND ALL THE GOLF ITEMS

CIRCLE THEM

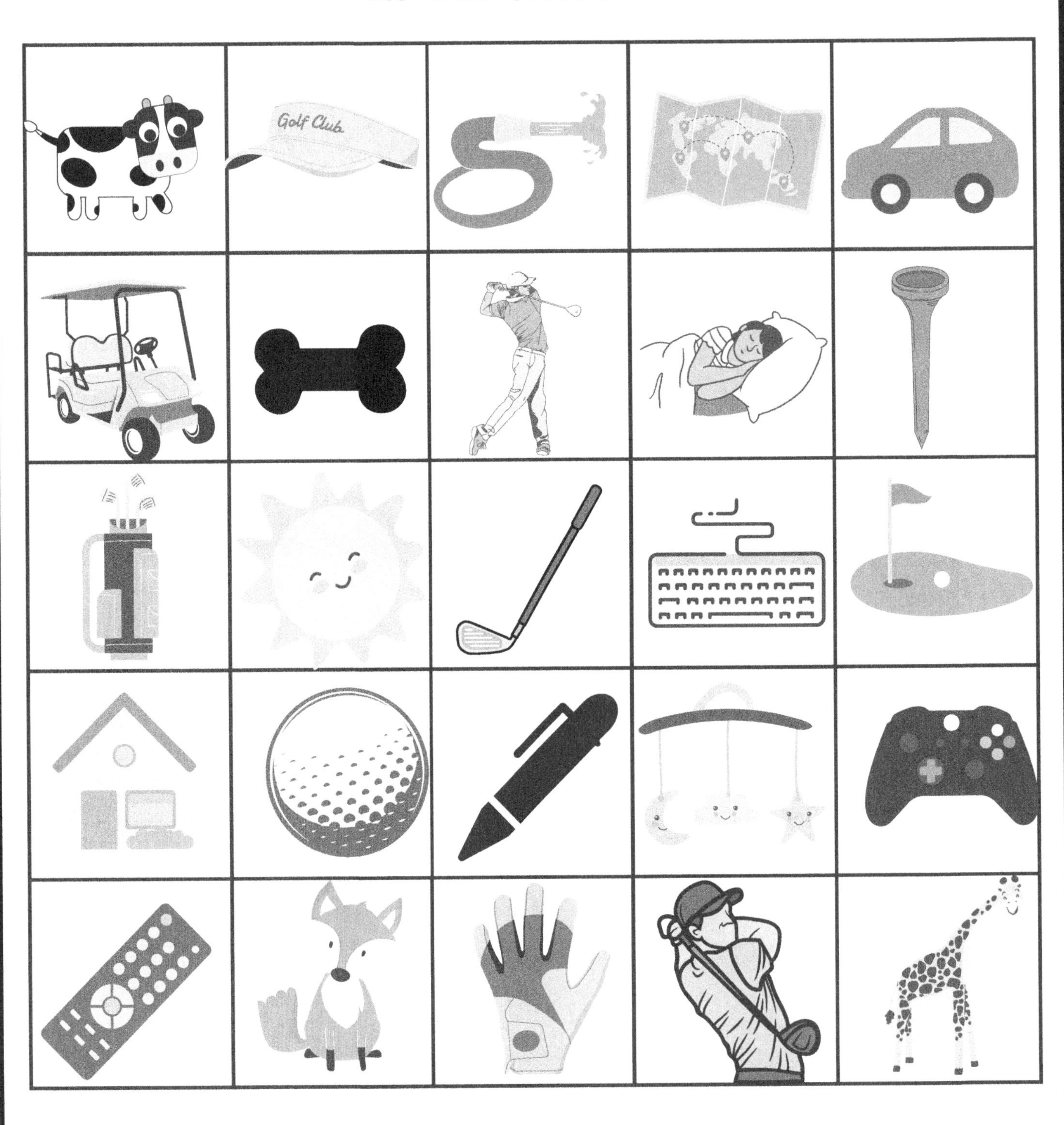

THERE ARE 10 TO FIND

GO ROUND THE GOLF COURSE AND COMPLETE THE COURSE TO WIN

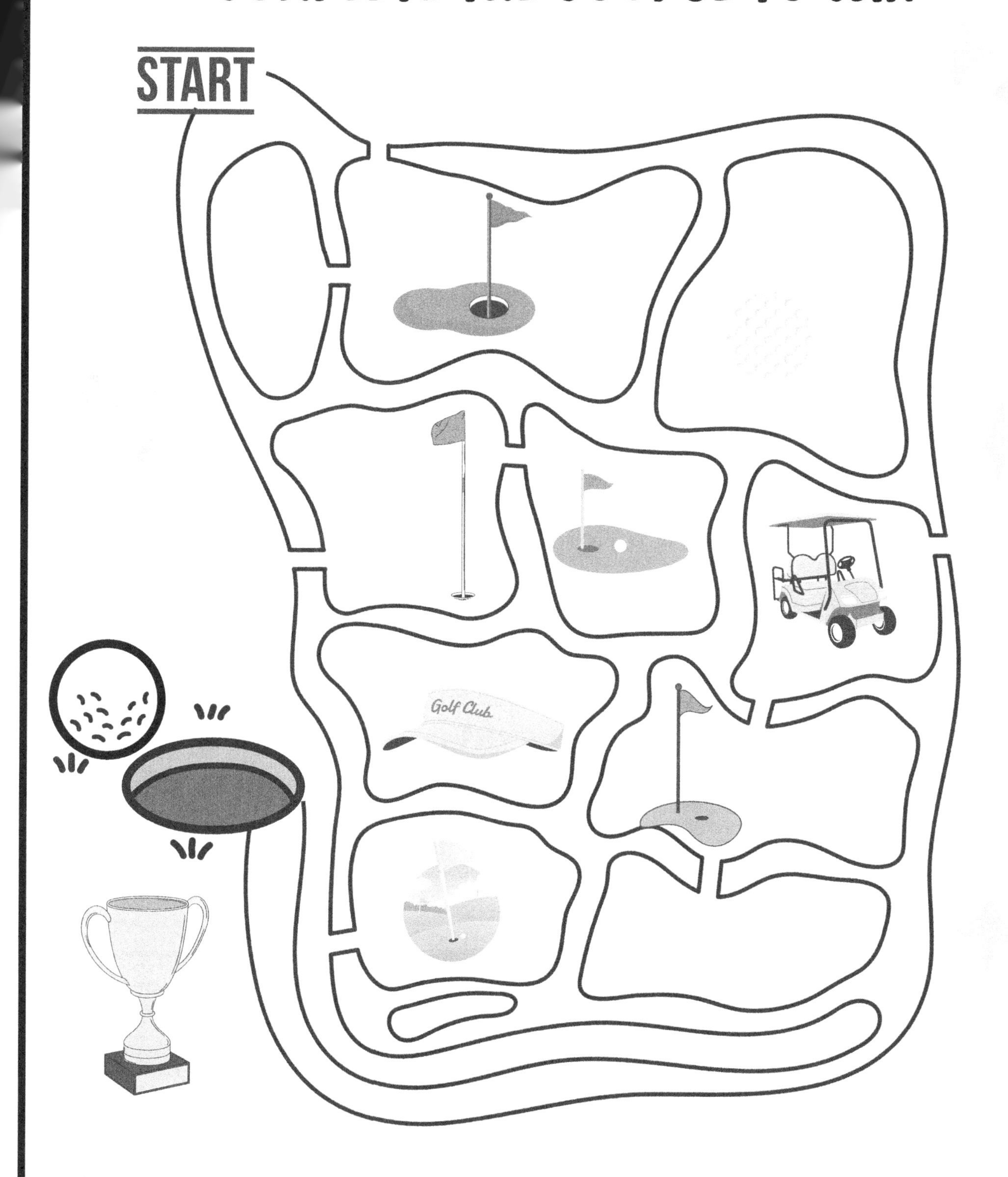

GET A HOLE IN ONE AND WIN THE CUP

CAN YOU COUNT HOW MANY OF EACH?

PUT THE ANSWER IN THE BOXES BELOW

CAN YOU HIT THE BALL IN
THE HOLE?
DON'T HIT IT TOO FAR THE
ALLIGATOR WILL GET IT
Solution 5

PICTURE SUDOKU

THIS IS PICTURE GOLF SUDOKU, PUT EACH ITEM IN SO THEY APPEAR

ONCE IN EACH OF THE BELOW- DRAW THEM IN

Medium

TIME FOR A HOLE IN ONE

GET TO THE GREEN

CHOOSE THE CORRECT GOLFER TO HIT THE BALL IN THE HOLE

AVOID HITTING INTO THE ALLIGATORS

Solution 7

WHAT IS THERE MORE OF

CART OR CLUB BAG

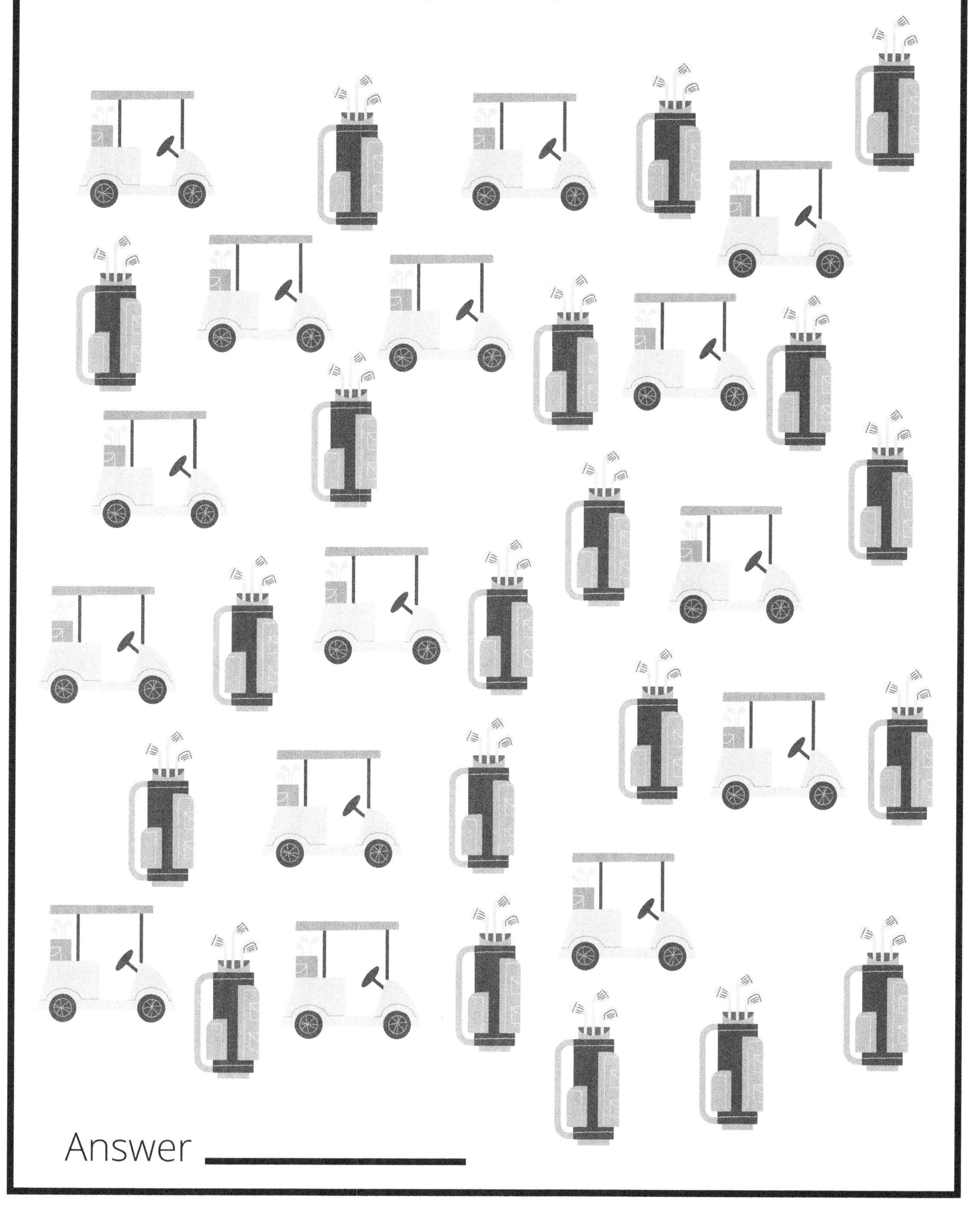

Answer ____________________

CAN YOU WORK OUT THE EQUATIONS

IF YOU NEED HELP ASK A GROWN UP

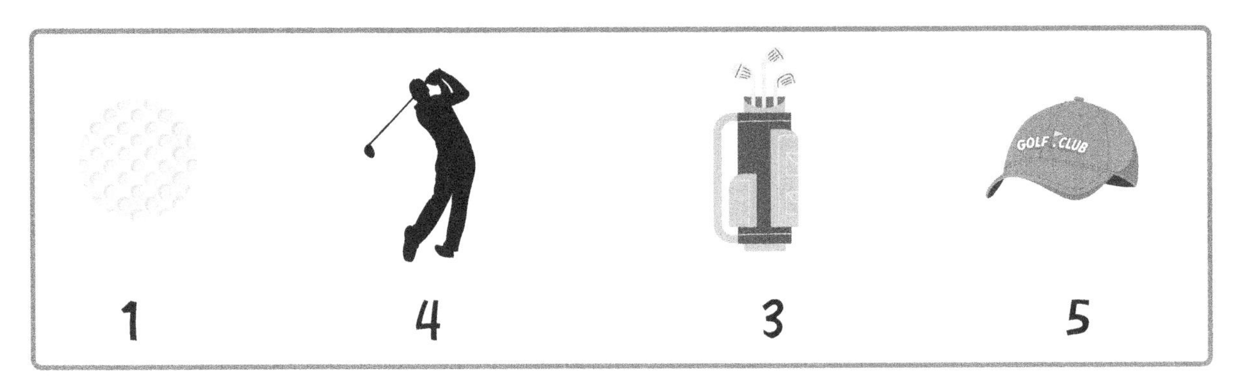

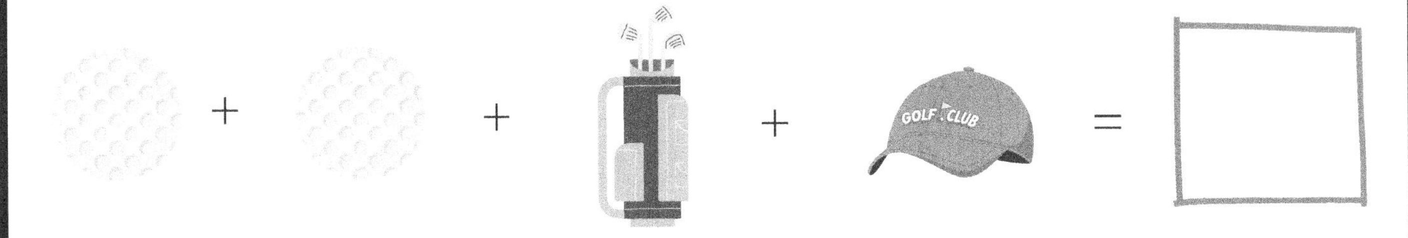

GOLF CLUB + GOLF CLUB + GOLF CLUB - - =

START

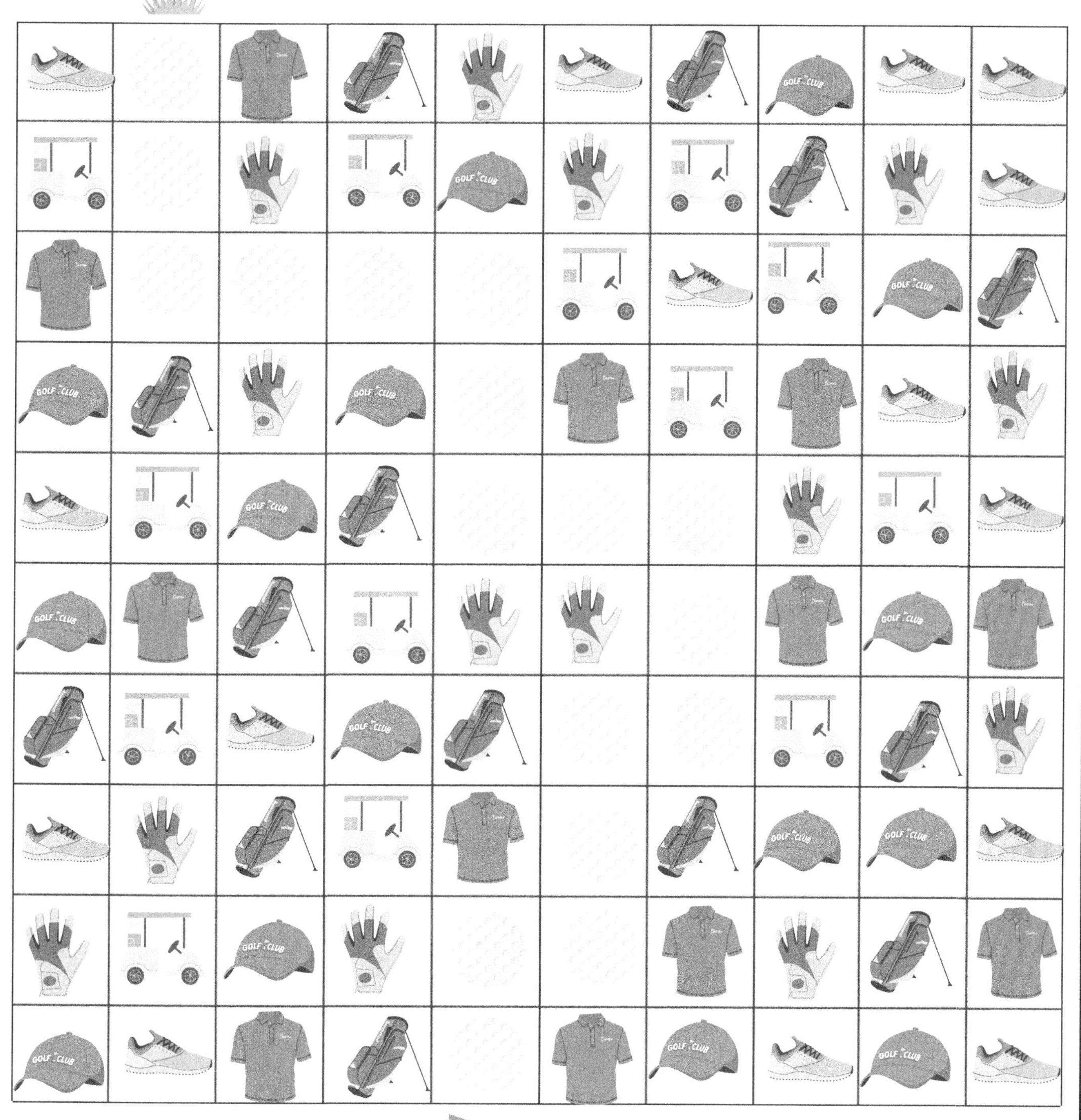

FINISH

TRACE THE WORDS EXERCISE

STAY IN THE LINES

Golf

Caddie

Birdie

Shot

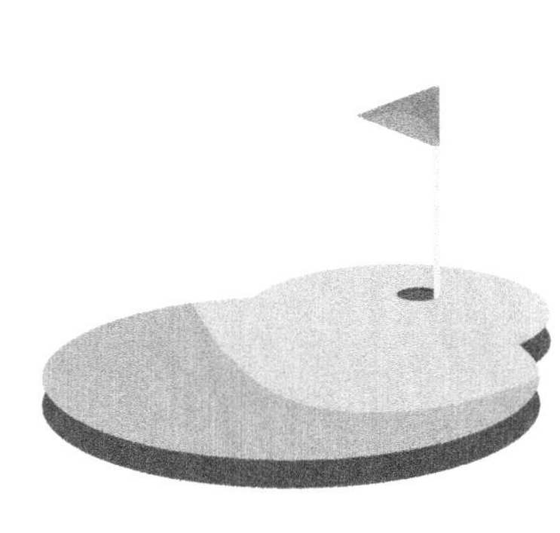

Green

Hole

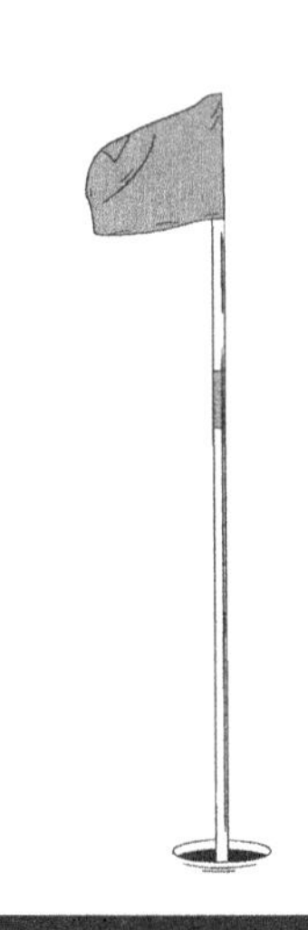

Flag

SOME FUN GOLF FACTS

1. LONGEST RECORDED DRIVE WAS 515 YARDS
2. FIRST 18-HOLE COURSE WAS ON A SHEEP FARM
3. GOLF BALLS WERE ORIGINALLY MADE OF WOOD

4. OTHER GOLF BALLS WERE MADE OF FEATHERS
5. GOLF WAS INVENTED IN SCOTLAND

6. THERE'S A 12,500 TO 1 CHANCE OF MAKING A HOLE-IN-ONE
7. THE FIRST ROUND OF WOMEN'S GOLF WAS PLAYED IN 1811

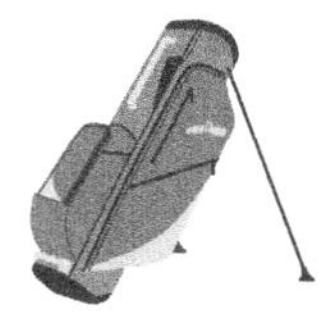

HELP THE GOLFER FIND A HOLE IN ONE

NAME EACH OF THESE GOLF ITEMS

....

....

....

....

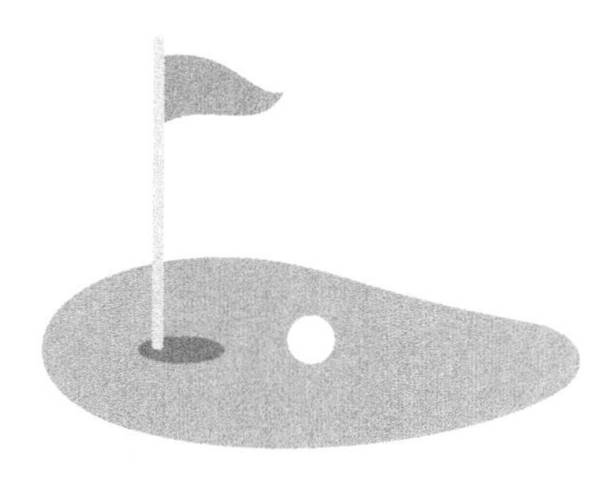

....

....

COMPLETE THE MAZE

GET TO THE MIDDLE

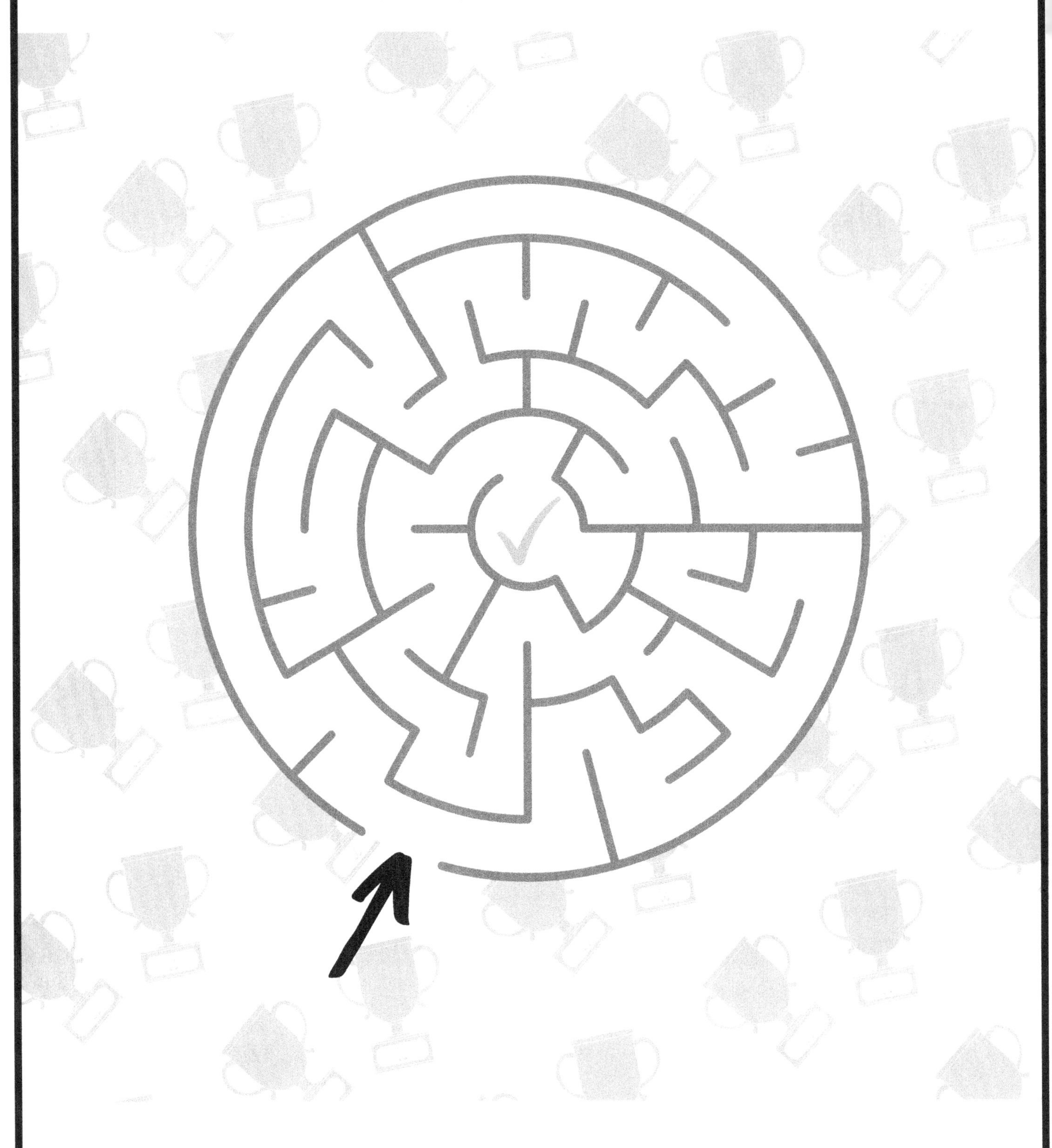

CAN YOU UNSCRAMBLE THESE GOLF WORDS

HINTS ARE PROVIDED OR ASK A GROWN UP TO HELP

OGLF — G _ _ _

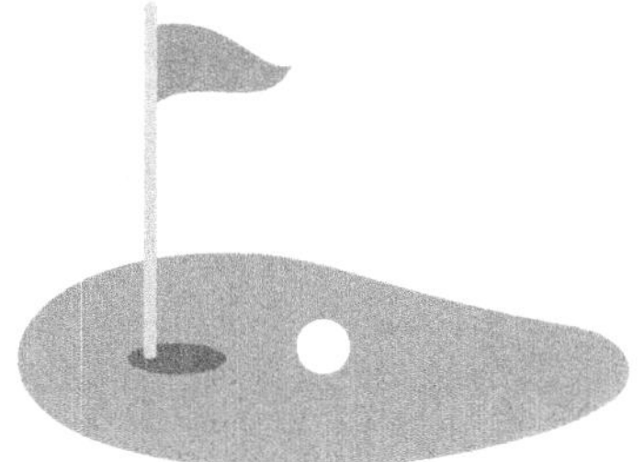

TCRA — C _ _ _

PCU — C _ _

ULBC — C _ _ B

TKSROE — S T _ _ _ E

NEEGR — G _ E _ _

LALB — B _ _ L

ETE — T _ _

COMPLETE THE MAZE

COMPLETE THE MAZE

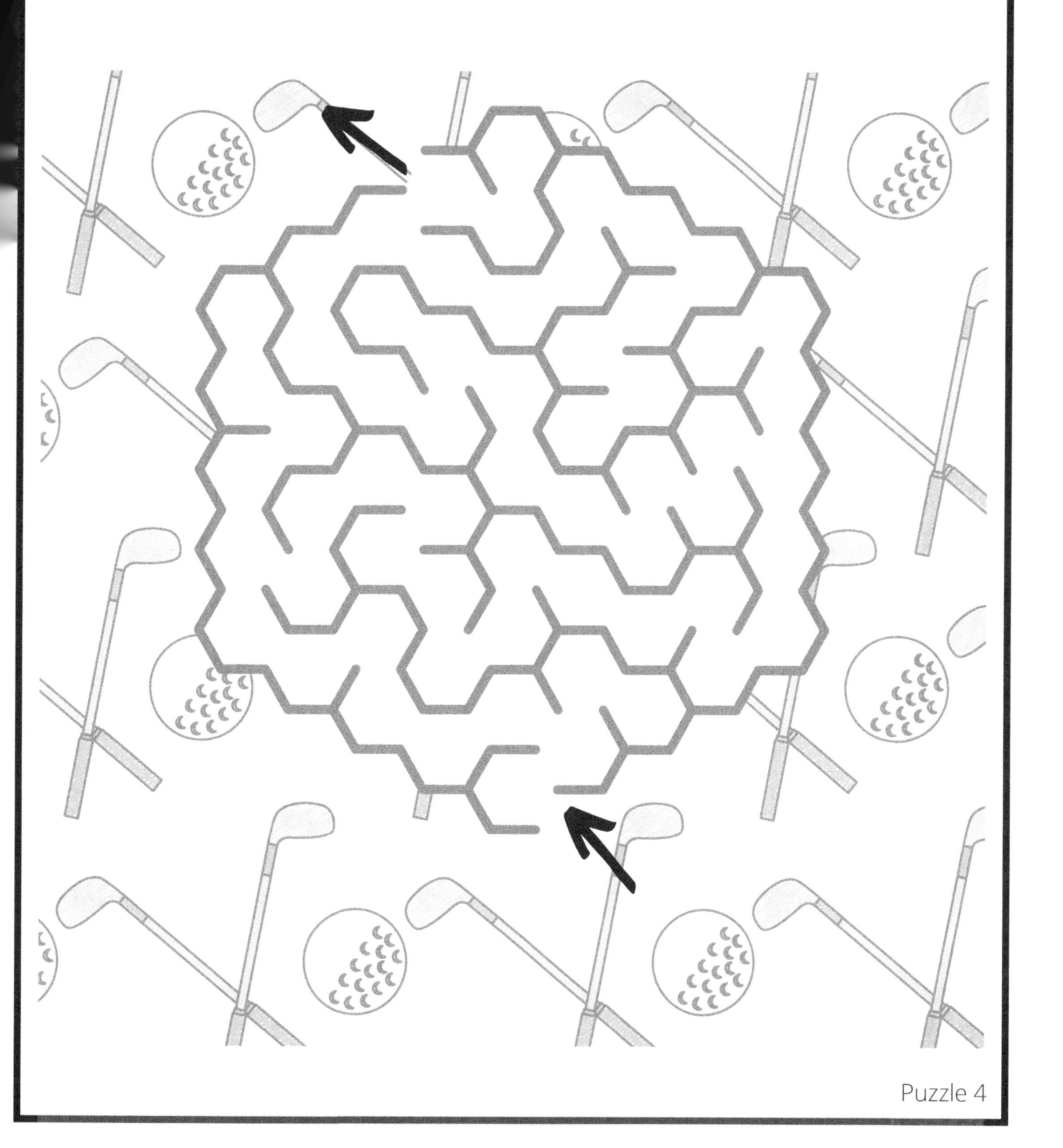

COMPLETE THE MAZE

COLLECT YOUR GOLF SHOES AND GLOVE

COMPLETE THE MAZE

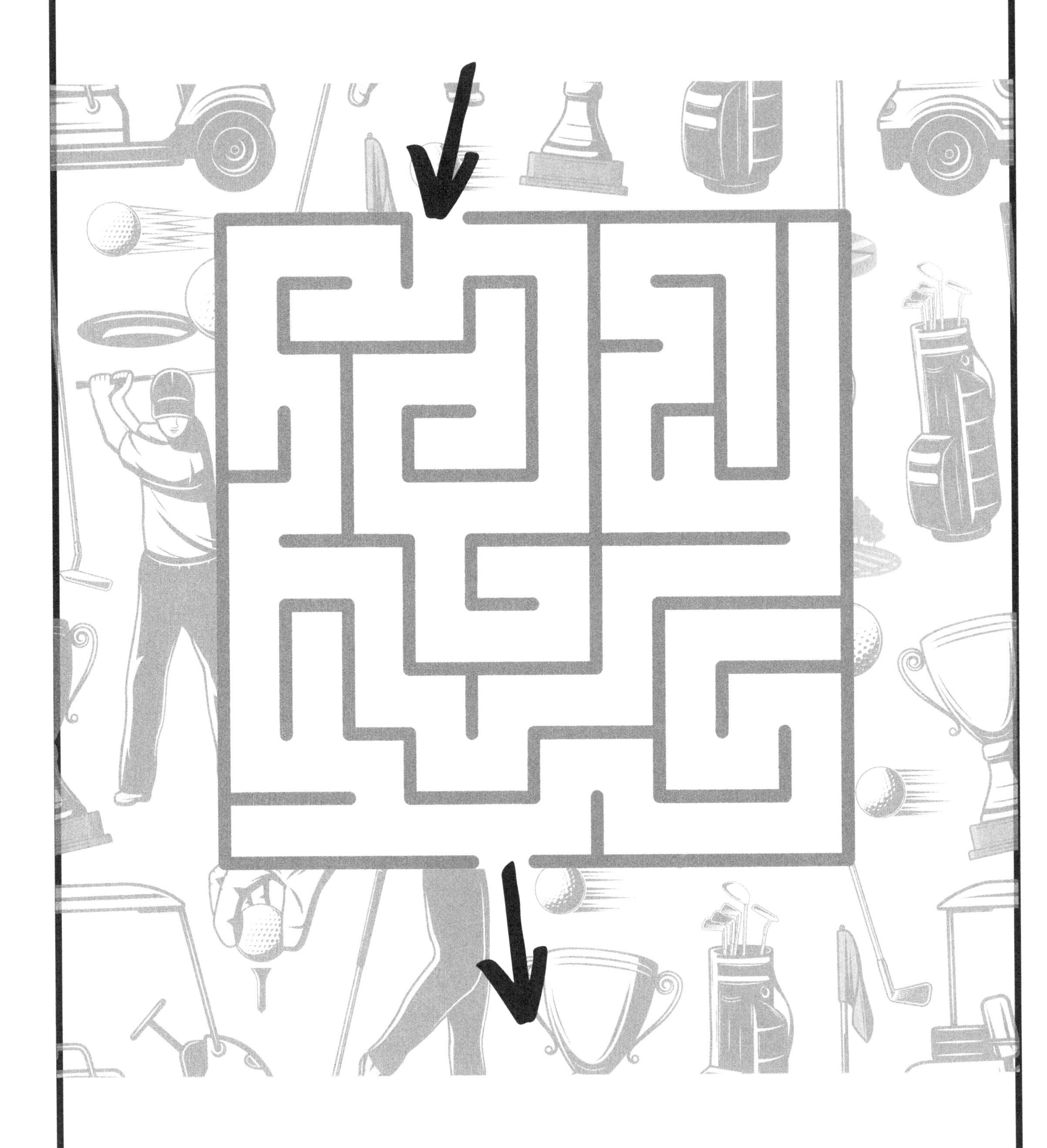

FIND THE GOLF WORDS

W	H	U	E	B	O	K	H	Z	N	W	D
M	O	G	U	F	P	A	O	R	U	G	V
H	O	L	K	U	T	R	L	K	I	V	E
Q	C	B	C	O	E	R	E	C	Y	L	L
Z	G	T	L	G	G	N	Q	W	H	F	I
I	H	N	Z	G	O	C	I	D	F	D	M
R	S	Q	X	M	P	L	A	C	G	C	I
J	C	T	L	J	G	C	F	R	K	X	C
V	V	A	R	F	P	G	O	N	T	F	E
U	V	U	K	O	S	Y	P	E	R	J	Y
X	U	U	B	V	K	K	L	T	C	V	O
W	L	O	S	H	X	E	G	X	R	W	T

CART
CUP
HOLE

CLUB
GOLF
STROKE

FIND THE GOLF WORDS

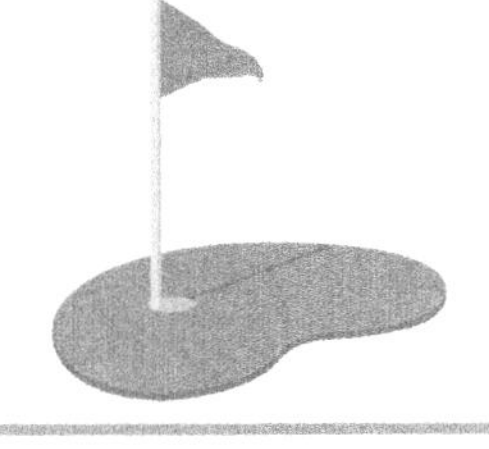

H	Y	B	V	W	D	J	F	R	O	G	S
S	R	C	A	D	D	I	E	Z	G	H	N
E	E	W	O	E	L	E	I	P	A	R	C
G	A	B	I	R	L	M	C	Q	F	S	Z
B	N	D	M	G	I	G	X	B	W	P	F
X	Z	D	A	D	R	E	Z	H	R	U	L
B	V	E	Z	D	O	B	R	H	J	T	Z
W	I	A	T	K	N	G	Q	N	H	T	T
U	W	R	W	C	B	A	W	A	Z	E	X
W	A	M	D	K	X	P	L	D	X	R	Z
F	L	N	I	I	N	P	L	N	O	M	L
Q	V	H	N	D	E	D	O	D	H	F	V

BIRDIE
EAGLE
PAR

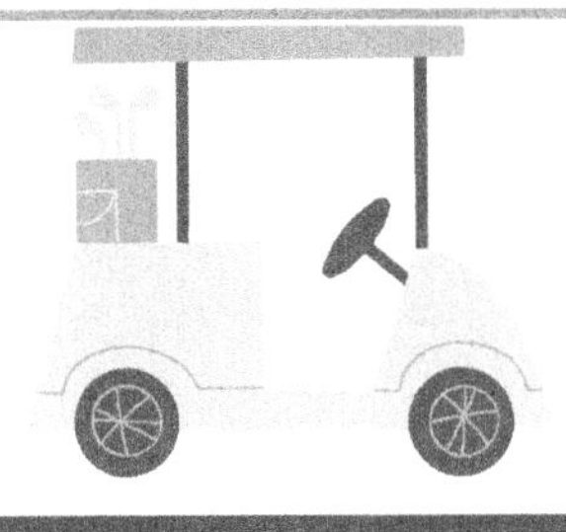

CADDIE
IRON
PUTTER

FIND THE GOLF WORDS

W	F	Y	P	G	T	B	Z	Y	H	C	D
D	E	E	K	O	T	I	D	Y	H	L	S
T	G	B	H	I	H	G	N	P	D	S	O
K	R	S	Q	A	Y	U	G	A	V	M	V
B	E	C	L	S	T	R	I	K	E	T	F
J	E	B	B	J	E	L	W	V	P	N	C
I	N	I	O	N	Q	S	F	Q	K	W	U
O	O	J	X	G	F	I	L	M	B	I	K
B	G	O	M	O	E	L	O	I	R	F	J
M	Q	M	O	I	I	Y	A	V	C	C	L
E	W	H	A	S	A	J	W	G	M	E	Y
F	K	A	D	U	C	W	M	L	D	P	J

BOGEY
GREEN
SLICE

FLAG
SHOT
STRIKE

FIND THE GOLF WORDS

W	R	U	A	U	F	E	I	G	H	T	I
O	P	Q	I	Q	I	Z	C	M	Q	J	D
U	M	U	L	N	R	M	F	I	V	E	K
Z	J	Q	E	H	H	O	Q	N	Q	Q	L
T	X	T	T	R	U	F	E	Q	J	T	S
F	N	Q	I	X	V	V	P	R	O	L	G
J	V	E	I	G	E	V	J	W	R	W	E
S	E	Y	H	S	T	O	J	R	C	F	S
R	O	H	I	R	N	R	N	H	X	A	J
T	C	N	I	K	C	R	B	I	P	X	T
B	F	S	E	T	E	K	C	O	N	V	S
M	W	Q	J	Z	O	I	V	F	L	E	R

EIGHT
NINE
SEVEN

FIVE
ONE
TEN

FIND THE GOLF WORDS

Z	C	M	Y	R	O	U	G	H	D	B	Z
A	X	J	S	K	V	A	E	F	V	H	A
L	L	D	E	K	W	A	T	Y	Y	X	B
C	F	X	Q	M	A	E	E	B	Z	D	J
X	V	B	Q	A	T	F	E	D	R	V	B
X	W	I	X	I	E	W	Y	A	S	D	C
G	X	I	G	M	R	U	Z	J	G	X	T
S	O	U	B	M	L	A	S	H	L	U	V
J	T	Q	R	E	H	U	Q	L	A	D	S
F	B	A	O	H	B	W	A	Z	W	J	W
H	W	F	U	Q	V	B	R	V	G	I	G
B	G	C	M	N	I	U	C	Q	Z	H	A

BALL
ROUGH
WARM

HAZARD
TEE
WATER

FIND THE GOLF WORDS

L	N	O	R	P	F	W	V	Y	W	O	C
F	U	I	G	E	V	T	G	W	N	B	C
M	Q	W	Q	B	G	M	I	K	P	M	W
L	W	T	N	G	S	L	R	I	L	K	T
W	E	Y	O	P	R	U	W	D	V	H	D
O	Q	B	L	E	H	I	K	Z	Z	E	C
D	Y	N	V	S	D	S	P	K	G	E	A
T	A	P	R	W	E	E	W	J	A	L	U
K	B	U	N	K	E	R	Q	I	Y	X	U
C	J	F	P	S	G	V	J	S	N	J	U
G	A	I	E	N	L	U	F	O	A	G	U
B	W	E	D	G	E	K	R	S	L	I	W

BUNKER
HEEL
TOE

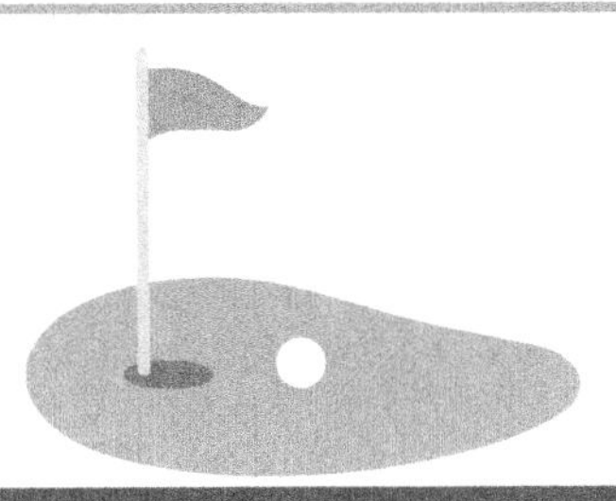

GRIP
SWING
WEDGE

CAN YOU MATCH THE CORRECT SHADOW

DESIGN YOUR OWN GOLF SHIRT AND GOLF SHOES

COLOR THEM IN

COMPLETE THE PICTURE OF THE GOLF CLUBS

COMPLETE THE PICTURE OF THE HOLE

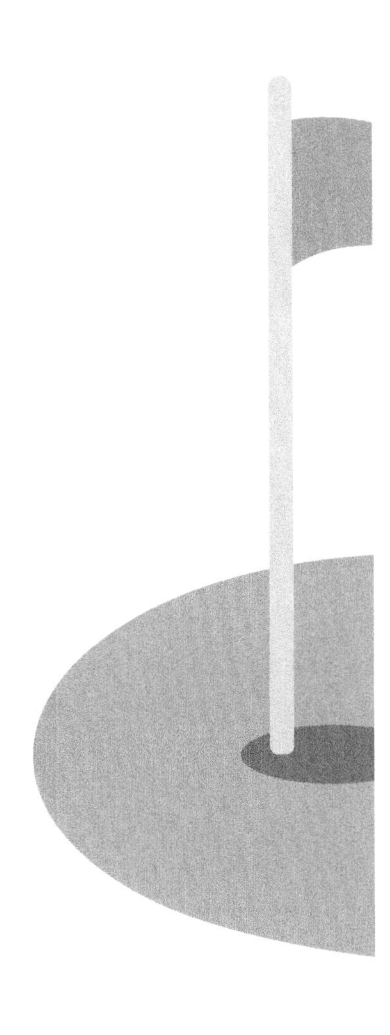

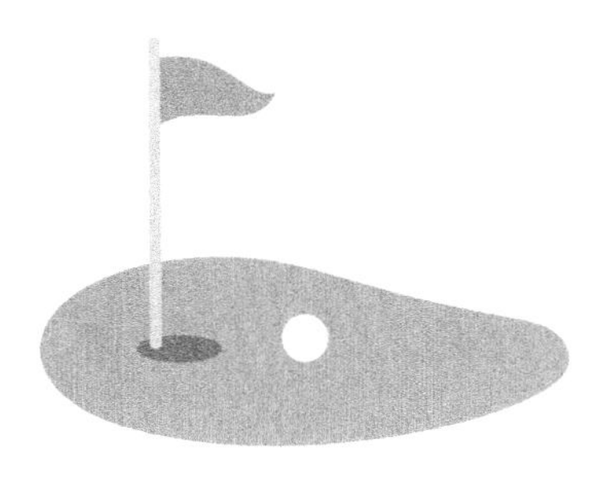

DESIGN YOUR OWN GOLF SHIRT AND GOLF SHOES

COLOR THEM IN

COMPLETE THE PICTURE OF THE GOLF CART

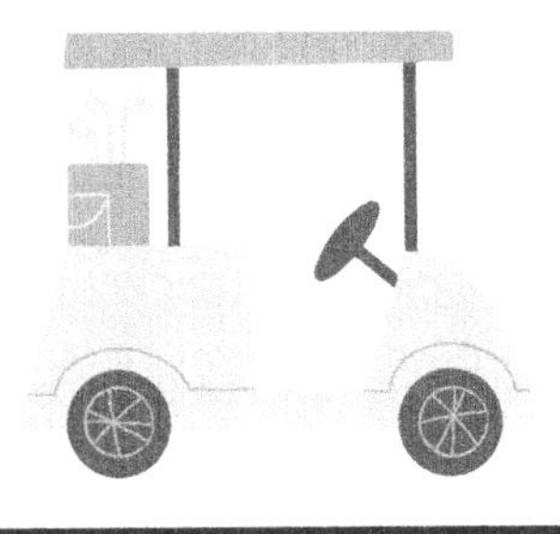

DESIGN YOUR OWN GOLF SHIRT AND GOLF SHOES

COLOR THEM IN

WHEN IS TEE OFF

CAN YOU TELL THE TIME, PICK THE CORRECT ANSWER

1)
- Ⓐ 3:00
- Ⓑ 7:00
- Ⓒ 10:00

2)
- Ⓐ 7:00
- Ⓑ 4:00
- Ⓒ 2:00

3)
- Ⓐ 2:00
- Ⓑ 11:00
- Ⓒ 9:00

4)
- Ⓐ 7:00
- Ⓑ 8:00
- Ⓒ 5:00

5)
- Ⓐ 8:00
- Ⓑ 10:00
- Ⓒ 12:00

6)
- Ⓐ 12:00
- Ⓑ 10:00
- Ⓒ 6:00

7)
- Ⓐ 8:00
- Ⓑ 7:00
- Ⓒ 6:00

8)
- Ⓐ 11:00
- Ⓑ 12:00
- Ⓒ 1:00

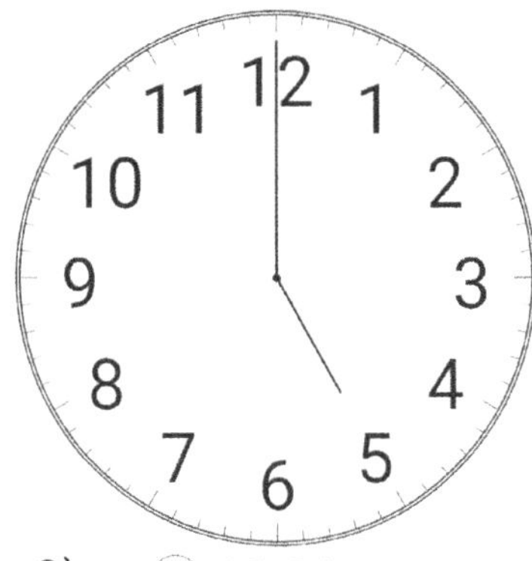

9)
- Ⓐ 12:00
- Ⓑ 5:00
- Ⓒ 9:00

HOW QUICK CAN YOU COMPLETE THE ADDITION PROBLEMS

YOUR TIME ☐

1) ☐ + 1 = 5

2) ☐ + 4 = 6

3) ☐ + 8 = 14

4) ☐ + 8 = 16

5) ☐ + 4 = 10

6) ☐ + 3 = 10

7) ☐ + 5 = 11

8) ☐ + 5 = 12

9) ☐ + 8 = 11

10) ☐ + 6 = 12

11) ☐ + 4 = 12

12) ☐ + 3 = 8

13) ☐ + 8 = 12

14) ☐ + 8 = 13

15) ☐ + 2 = 9

16) ☐ + 6 = 14

17) ☐ + 6 = 13

18) ☐ + 9 = 15

19) ☐ + 1 = 10

20) ☐ + 7 = 16

21) ☐ + 7 = 15

22) ☐ + 2 = 5

23) ☐ + 5 = 6

24) ☐ + 6 = 13

25) ☐ + 2 = 11

26) ☐ + 7 = 8

27) ☐ + 8 = 9

28) ☐ + 1 = 2

29) ☐ + 3 = 10

30) ☐ + 7 = 12

HOW QUICK CAN YOU COMPLETE THE SUBTRACTION PROBLEMS

YOUR TIME

1) 10 − 7	2) 8 − 6	3) 11 − 9	4) 11 − 8	5) 6 − 3
6) 12 − 9	7) 10 − 7	8) 9 − 1	9) 7 − 5	10) 9 − 6
11) 4 − 3	12) 11 − 5	13) 7 − 5	14) 10 − 2	15) 12 − 4
16) 11 − 1	17) 10 − 1	18) 4 − 4	19) 11 − 10	20) 10 − 9
21) 11 − 9	22) 11 − 6	23) 10 − 2	24) 7 − 5	25) 6 − 1
26) 5 − 4	27) 7 − 1	28) 9 − 2	29) 11 − 4	30) 5 − 1

HOW QUICK CAN YOU COMPLETE THE MULTIPLICATION PROBLEMS

YOUR TIME

1) 4×2	2) 7×6	3) 9×9	4) 5×1	5) 4×9
6) 4×3	7) 1×8	8) 7×2	9) 4×6	10) 2×6
11) 4×1	12) 6×7	13) 1×3	14) 3×4	15) 3×8
16) 2×3	17) 4×2	18) 9×3	19) 7×7	20) 3×2
21) 5×2	22) 9×5	23) 8×9	24) 4×2	25) 4×8
26) 1×7	27) 6×2	28) 3×1	29) 3×9	30) 2×6

GOLF CART

CLUB CAR

GOLF IS FUN

GREAT
SHOT

SWING

CERTIFICATE OF ACHIEVEMENT

THIS IS TO CERTIFY THAT

____

has completed the golf activity book and has done a great job

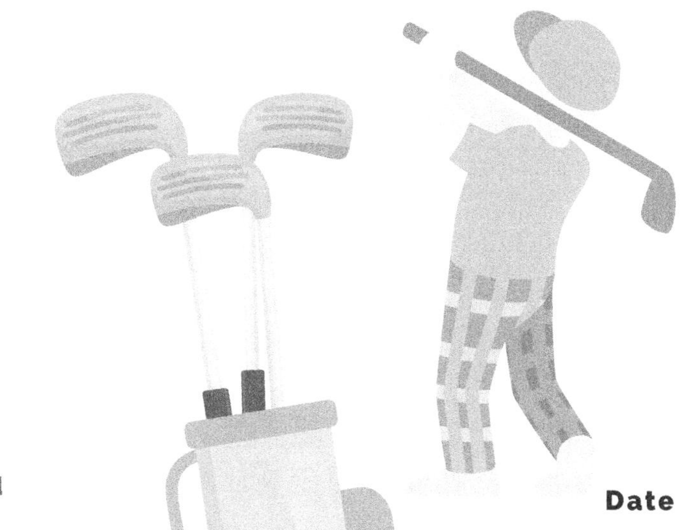

Signed

____

Date

____

SOLUTIONS

IF YOU NEED THEM

STORY MAZE ANSWERS

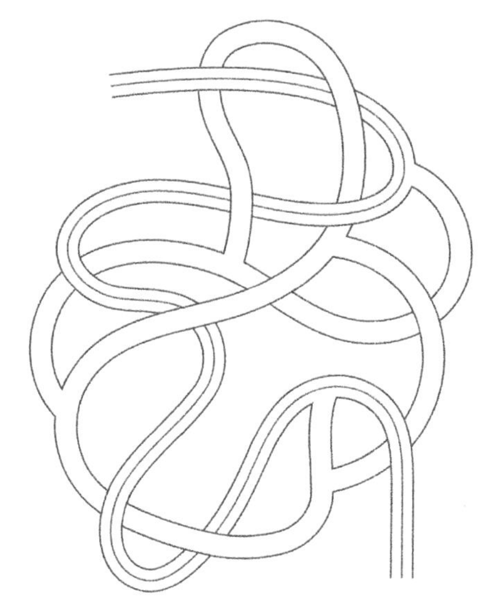

Solution 1

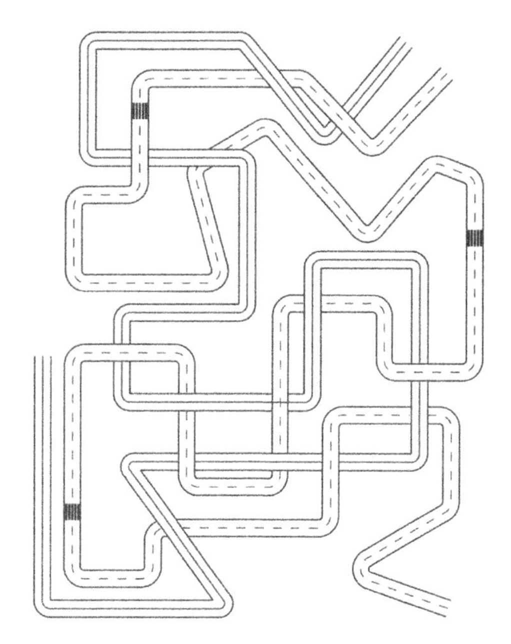

Solution 2

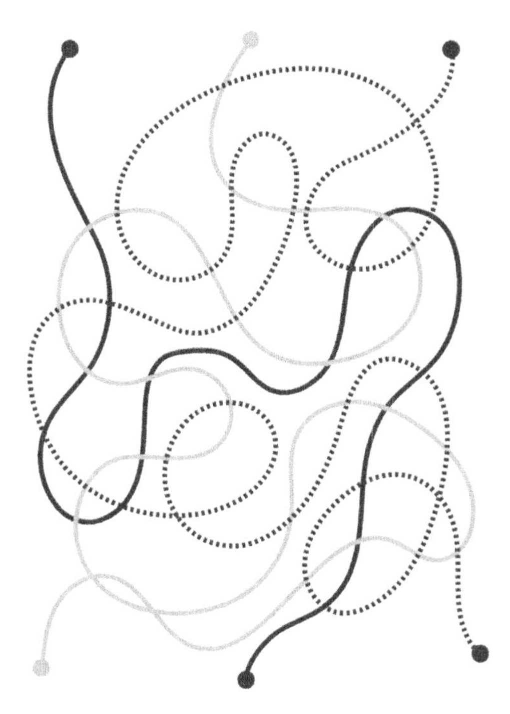

Solution 3

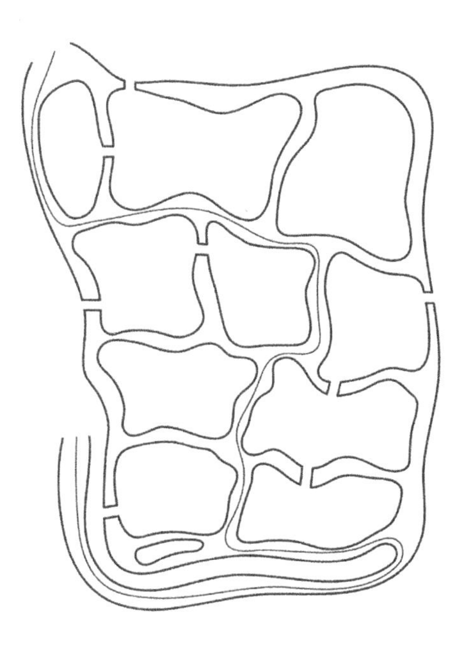

Solution 4

STORY MAZE ANSWERS

Solution 5

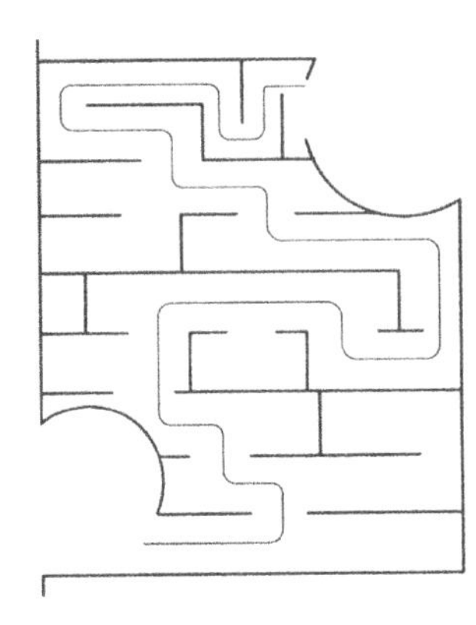

Solution 6

Solution 7

PICTURE SUDOKU ANSWER

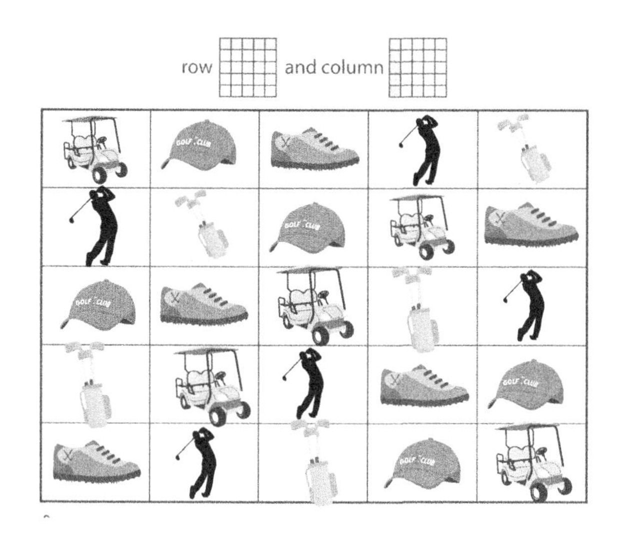

MATH ANSWER

IF YOU NEED HELP ASK A GROWN UP

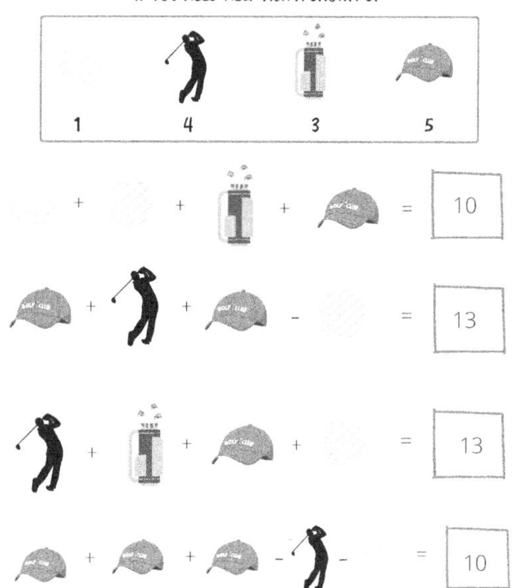

FOLLOW THE
TO COMPLETE THE GOLF SHOT

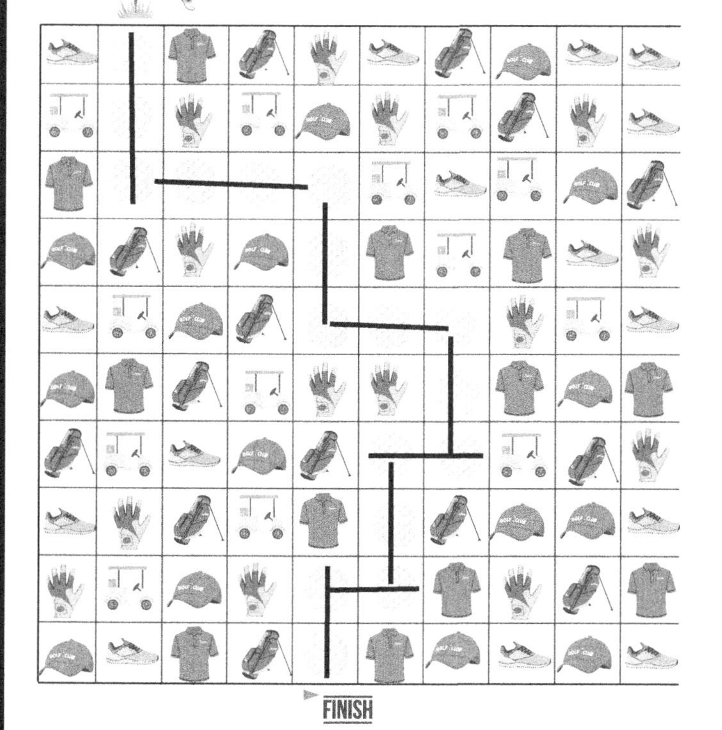

CAN YOU COUNT HOW MANY OF EACH?

PUT THE ANSWER IN THE BOXES BELOW

Unscramble the words answer

OGLF	GOLF
TCRA	CART
PCU	CUP
ULBC	CLUB
TKSROE	STROKE
NEEGR	GREEN
LALB	BALL
ETE	TEE

FIND ALL THE GOLF ITEMS ANSWERS

THERE ARE 10 TO FIND

CART 15

CLUB BAG 20

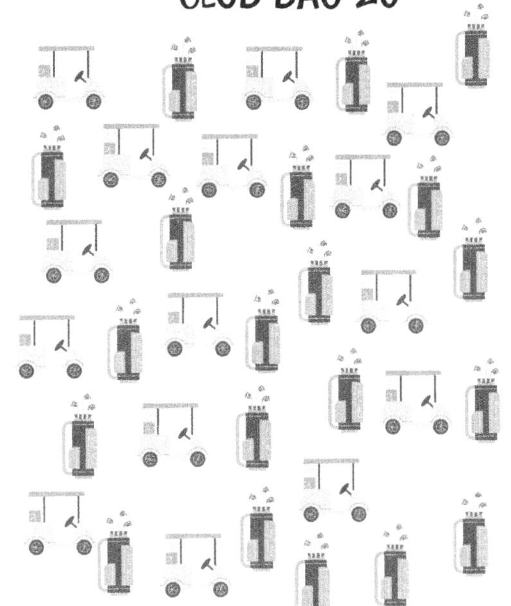

NAME EACH OF THESE GOLF ITEMS

Answers

Golf shoes

Golf club

Golf cart

Golf ball

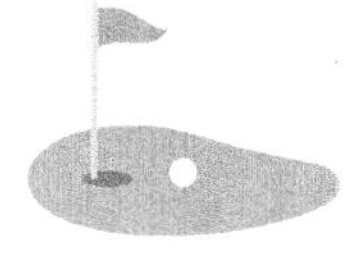

Golf green

Golf cap

CAN YOU FIND

CIRCLE IT

CAN YOU FIND THE ODD GOLFER OUT?

CAN YOU MATCH THE CORRECT SHADOW

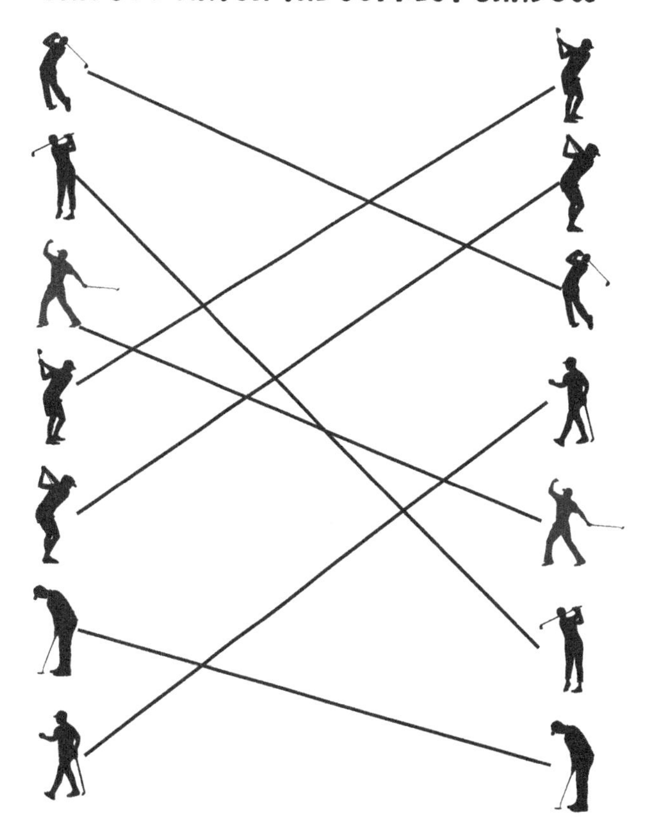

WORD SEARCH ANSWERS

Puzzle #1 – Solution

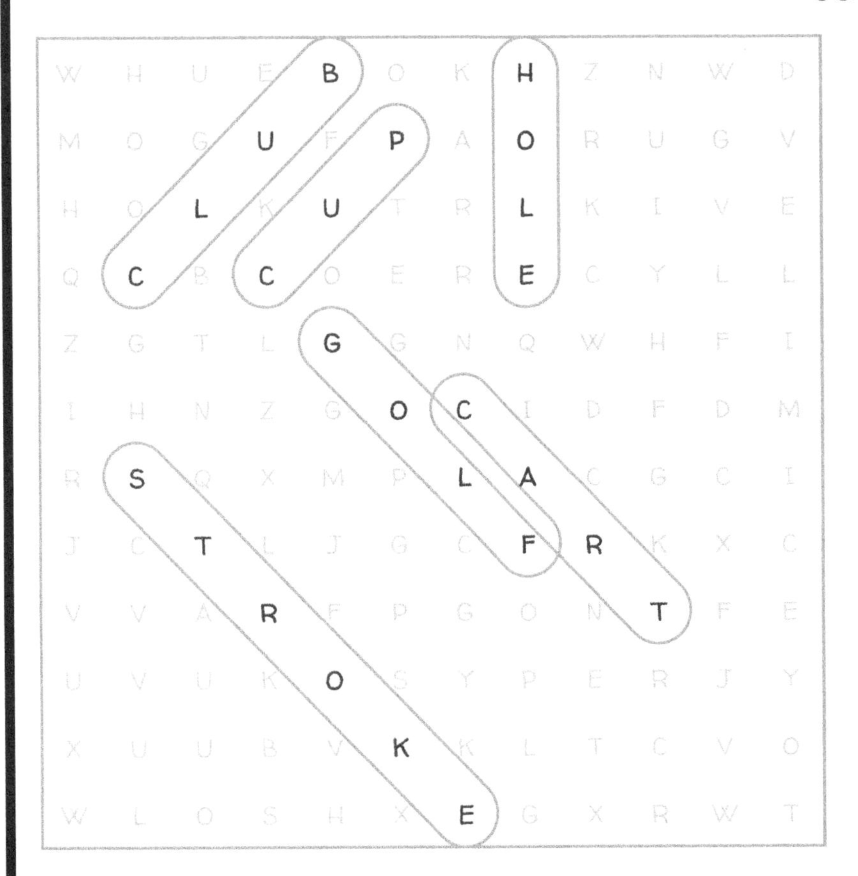

Puzzle #2 – Solution

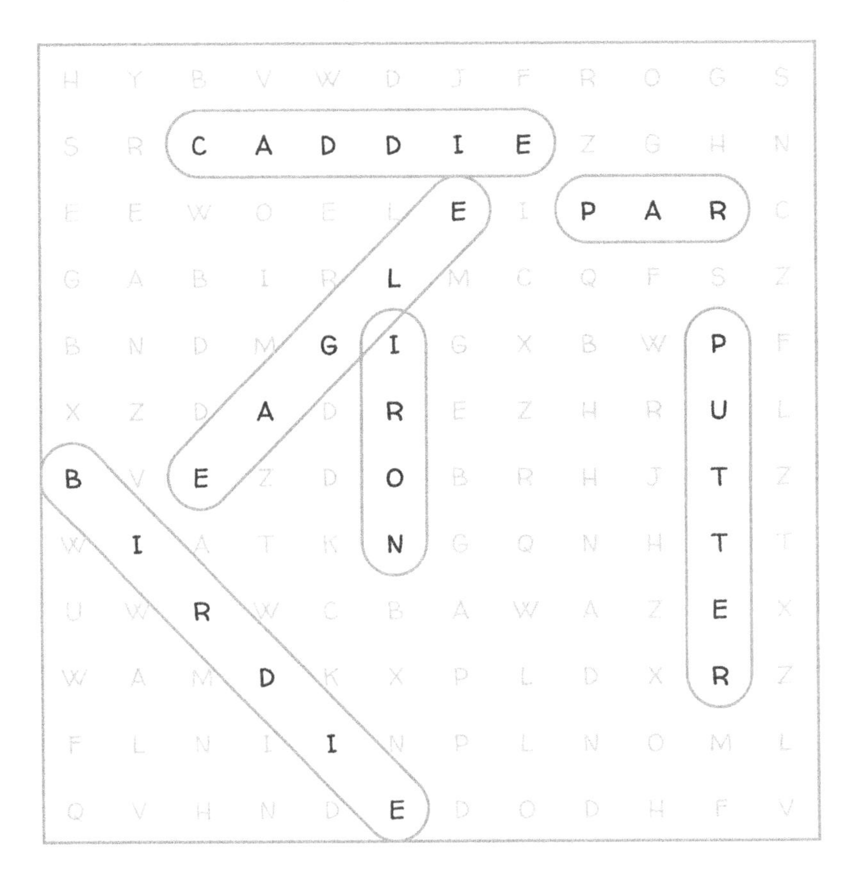

WORD SEARCH ANSWERS

Puzzle #3 – Solution

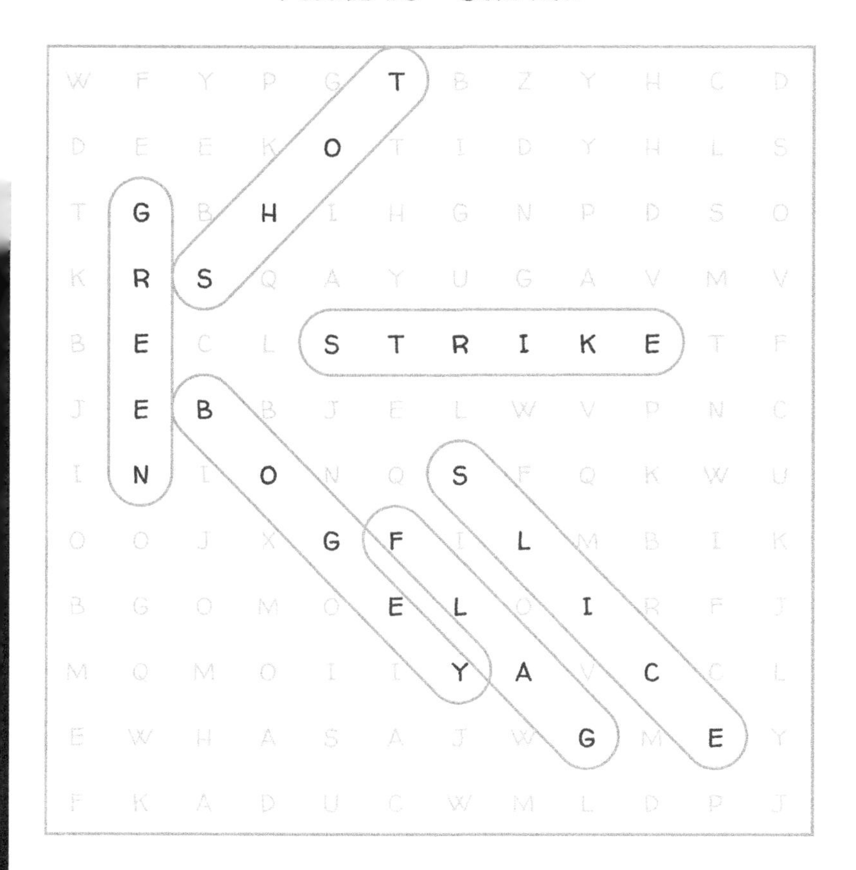

Puzzle #4 – Solution

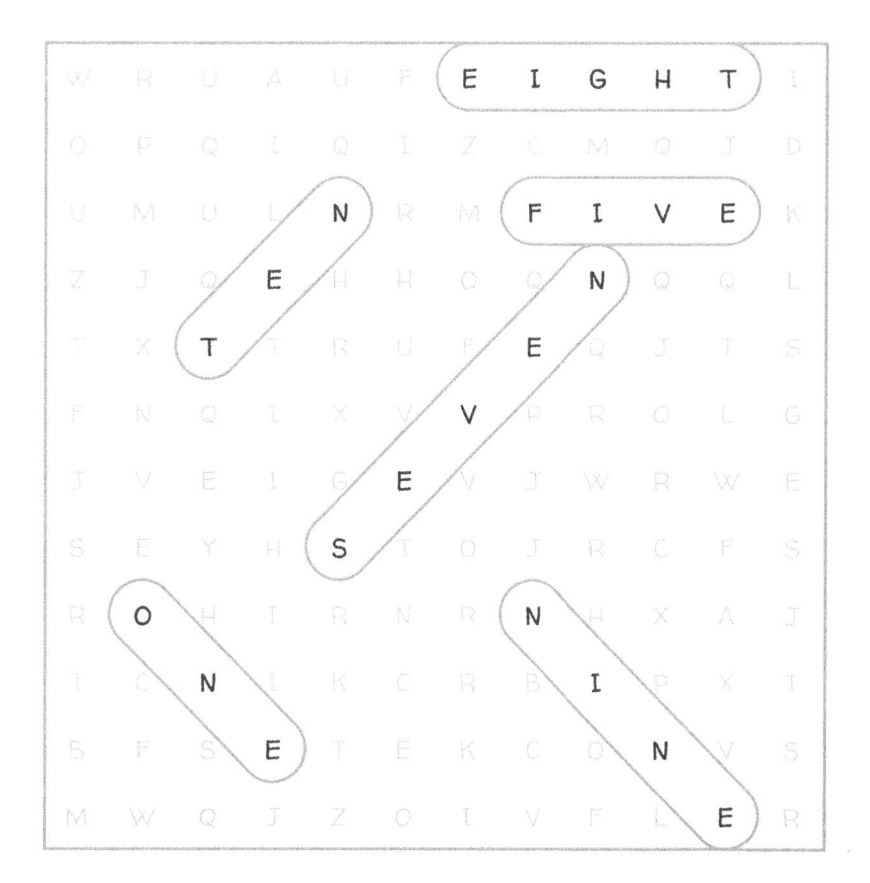

WORD SEARCH ANSWERS

Puzzle #5 – Solution

Z	C	M	Y	R	O	U	G	H	D	B	Z
A	X	J	S	K	V	A	E	F	V	H	A
L	L	D	E	K	W	A	T	Y	Y	X	B
C	F	X	Q	M	A	E	E	B	Z	D	J
X	V	B	Q	A	T	F	E	D	R	V	B
X	W	I	X	I	E	W	Y	A	S	D	C
G	X	I	G	M	R	U	Z	J	G	X	T
S	O	U	B	M	L	A	S	H	L	U	V
J	T	Q	R	E	H	U	Q	L	A	D	S
F	B	A	O	H	B	W	A	Z	W	J	W
H	W	F	U	Q	V	B	R	V	G	I	G
B	G	C	M	N	I	U	C	Q	Z	H	A

Puzzle #6 – Solution

L	N	O	R	P	F	W	V	Y	W	O	C
F	U	I	G	E	V	T	G	W	N	B	C
M	Q	W	Q	B	G	M	I	K	P	M	W
L	W	T	N	G	S	L	R	I	L	K	T
W	E	Y	O	P	R	U	W	D	V	H	D
O	Q	B	L	E	H	I	K	Z	Z	E	C
D	Y	N	V	S	D	S	P	K	G	E	A
T	A	P	R	W	E	E	W	J	A	L	U
K	B	U	N	K	E	R	Q	I	Y	X	U
C	J	F	P	S	G	V	J	S	N	J	U
G	A	I	E	N	L	U	F	O	A	G	U
B	W	E	D	G	E	K	R	S	L	I	W

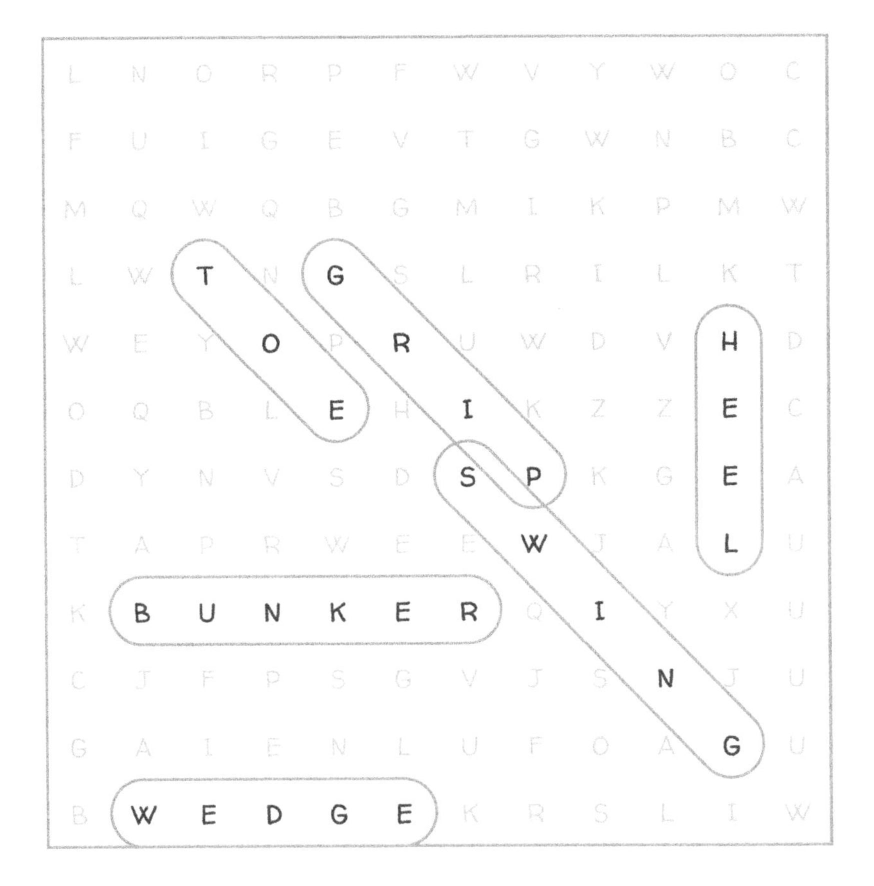

SHAPED MAZE ANSWERS

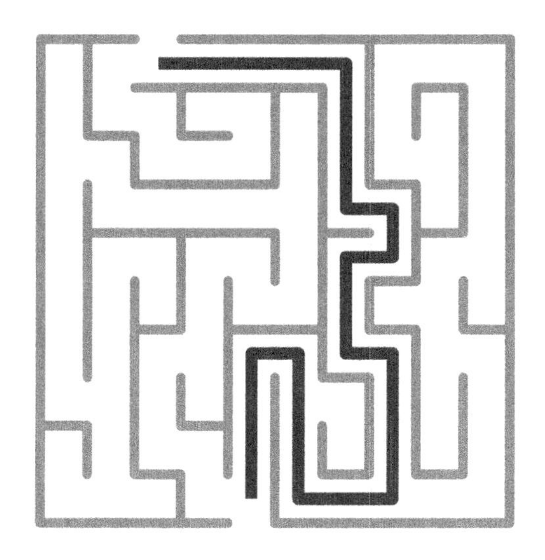

Puzzle 1

Puzzle 2

Puzzle 3

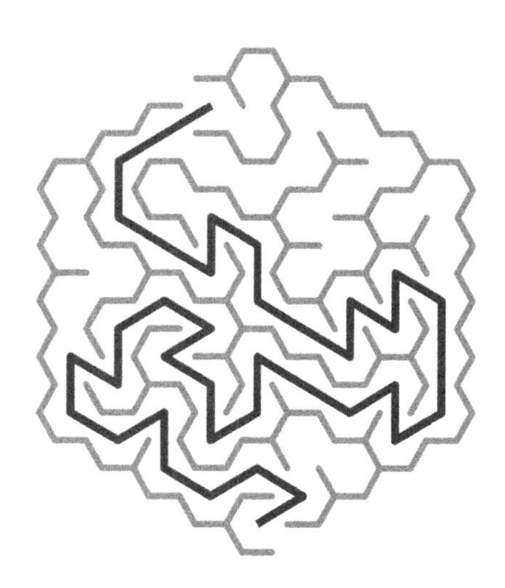

Puzzle 4

SHAPED MAZE ANSWERS

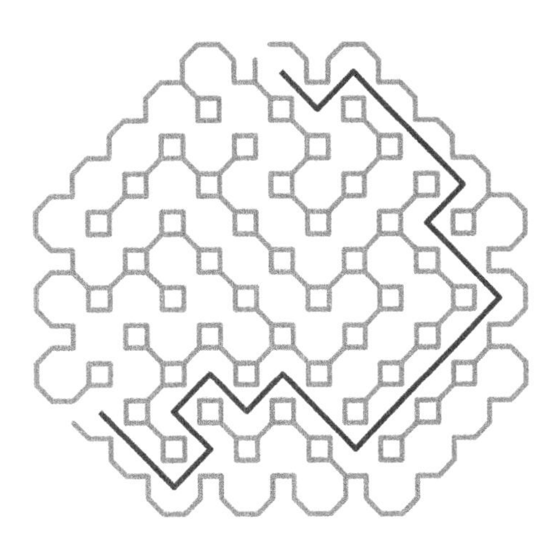

Puzzle 5

Puzzle 6

Puzzle 7

Math answers

Page 1, Item 1: **Telling the time**

(1)B (2)A (3)C (4)A (5)B (6)B (7)C (8)C (9)B

Page 2, Item 1: **Addition**

(1)4 (2)2 (3)6 (4)8 (5)6 (6)7 (7)6 (8)7 (9)3
(10)6 (11)8 (12)5 (13)4 (14)5 (15)7 (16)8
(17)7 (18)6 (19)9 (20)9 (21)8 (22)3 (23)1
(24)7 (25)9 (26)1 (27)1 (28)1 (29)7 (30)5

Page 3, Item 2: **Subtraction**

(1)3 (2)2 (3)2 (4)3 (5)3 (6)3 (7)3 (8)8 (9)2
(10)3 (11)1 (12)6 (13)2 (14)8 (15)8 (16)10
(17)9 (18)0 (19)1 (20)1 (21)2 (22)5 (23)8
(24)2 (25)5 (26)1 (27)6 (28)7 (29)7 (30)4

Page 4, Item 1: **Multiplication**

(1)8 (2)42 (3)81 (4)5 (5)36 (6)12 (7)8 (8)14
(9)24 (10)12 (11)4 (12)42 (13)3 (14)12
(15)24 (16)6 (17)8 (18)27 (19)49 (20)6
(21)10 (22)45 (23)72 (24)8 (25)32 (26)7
(27)12 (28)3 (29)27 (30)12

Made in the USA
Monee, IL
08 July 2023

38840001R00050